bl as in blaze

Write and say **bl**_____ **bl**_____ **bl**_____ **bl**_____

Add **bl** to make twenty words.

bl — **ind** ________
bl — **ink** ________
bl — **ade** ________
bl — **end** ________
bl — **anket** ________

bl — **ame** ________
bl — **eep** ________
bl — **ack** ________
bl — **ast** ________
bl — **ossom** ________

bl — **ast-off** ________
bl — **each** ________
bl — **azer** ________
bl — **unt** ________
bl — **ackbird** ________

bl — **aze** ________
bl — **ue** ________
bl — **ood** ________
bl — **ock** ________
bl — **izzard** ________

Write the correct word under each picture.

________ ________ ________ ________ ________

Use words you have made to complete these sentences.

Hurry up! Don't________ me if we miss the bus.

The windows were smashed by the________ of the explosion.

You can't cut that card with________ scissors.

The colour of the sky on a cloudless, sunny day is________ .

The computer will________ if you enter a wrong command.

Word Puzzle

opposite of white — b l ○ ○ ○
to mix together — b l ○ ○ ○
part of a knife used for cutting — b l ○ ○ ○
to make something white — b l ○ ○ ○ ○
open and close the eyes quickly — b l ○ ○ ○
a kind of jacket — b l ○ ○ ○ ○
flowers of a tree, e.g. apple — b l ○ ○ ○ ○ ○
to burn brightly — b l ○ ○ ○

and Spell

blast ______
bleep ______
blend ______
blame ______
blink ______
blue ______
blood ______
black ______
blazer ______
blind ______
bleach ______
blunt ______
blade ______
blaze ______
block ______
blast-off ______
blanket ______
blizzard ______
blossom ______
blackbird ______

fl as in flower

Write and say **fl** ___fl___ **fl** ______ **fl** ______ **fl** ______

Add **fl** to make eighteen words.

eece	______	**amingo**	______
ask	______	**ippers**	______
y	______	**ag**	______
ower	______	**annel**	______
our	______	**orist**	______
op	______	**ood**	______
ock	______	**ute**	______
oat	______	**oor**	______
icker	______	**avour**	______

Write the correct word under each picture.

FRESH FLOWERS

______ ______ ______ ______ ______

Use words you have made to complete these sentences.

The ________ of the United Kingdom is sometimes called the Union Jack.

Kerry took some orange juice in a ________ for her lunch.

The farmer clipped the ________ from the sheep's back.

Water animals use their ________ like paddles to help them to swim.

Birds and insects ________ by moving their wings.

Crossword

Clues Across

2. a cloth used for washing yourself
4. part of a plant that has petals and produces seeds
5. a large group of sheep
6. powder made from wheat, used to make bread and cakes

Clues Down

1. the taste of something
2. shine with a blinking light
3. drop down suddenly
4. stay on surface of water and not sink

Read, Write, Learn, Cover and Spell

float	float
flour	______
fly	______
fleece	______
floor	______
flag	______
flask	______
flop	______
flood	______
flute	______
flicker	______
florist	______
flower	______
flock	______
flavour	______
flannel	______
flippers	______
flamingo	______

pl as in plant

Write and say **pl** ___ **pl** ___ **pl** ___ **pl** ___

Add **pl** to make sixteen words.

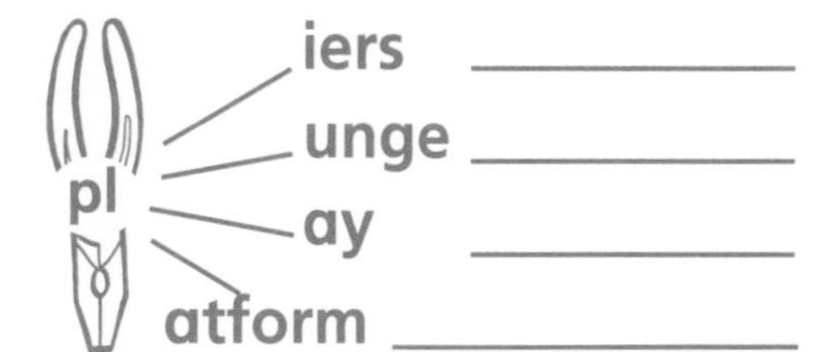

pl — **iers** ___ **unge** ___ **ay** ___ **atform** ___

pl — **umber** ___ **ayful** ___ **ug** ___ **easure** ___

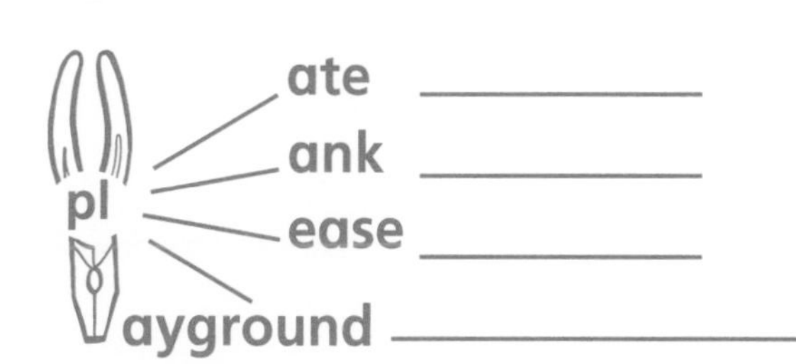

pl — **ate** ___ **ank** ___ **ease** ___ **ayground** ___

pl — **anet** ___ **ough** ___ **us** ___ **aice** ___

Write the correct word under each picture.

___ ___ ___ ___

Use words you have made to complete these sentences.

Eight ___ seven equals fifteen.

We waited on the ___ to catch the train.

When Samira asks for things,
she always says ___ .

Debra is learning to ___ the piano.

We sent for a ___ to mend the leaking water pipes.

Word Puzzle

full of fun	p l _ _ _ _ _
flat sea-fish used as food	p l _ _ _ _
a stopper for bath or sink	p l _ _
something that gives happiness	p l _ _ _ _ _ _
long, flat piece of wood	p l _ _ _
to dive in	p l _ _ _ _
flat dish for eating from	p l _ _ _

Read, Write, Learn, Cover and Spell

please please
plough ___
plaice ___
plunge ___
pliers ___
plus ___
plate ___
play ___
plug ___
planet ___
plank ___
pleasure ___
playground ___
plumber ___
playful ___
platform ___

as in **drum**

Write and say **dr** dr____ **dr** ____ **dr** ____ **dr** ____

Add **dr** to make eighteen words.

izzle ____________
um ____________
ake ____________
eam ____________
awer ____________

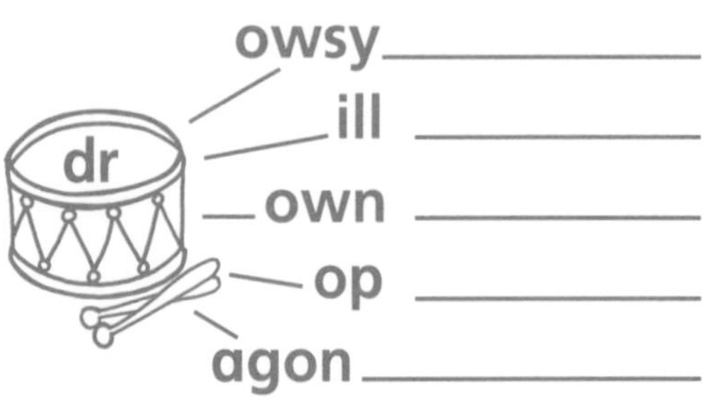

owsy ____________
ill ____________
own ____________
op ____________
agon ____________

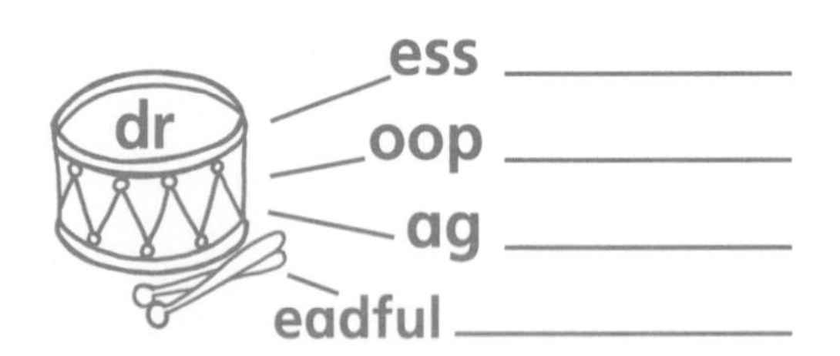

ess ____________
oop ____________
ag ____________
eadful ____________

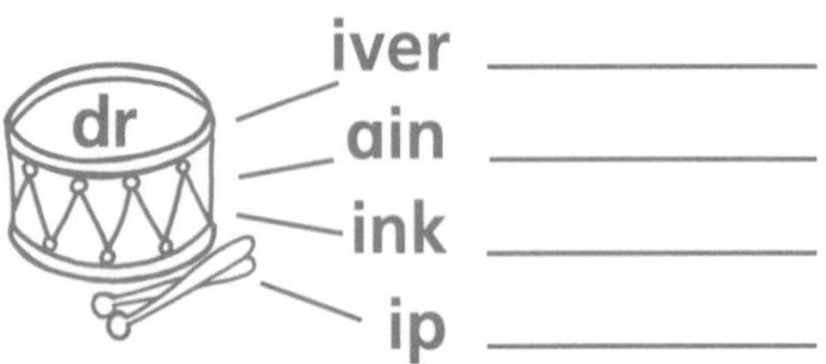

iver ____________
ain ____________
ink ____________
ip ____________

Write the correct word under each picture.

__________ __________ __________ __________ __________

Use words you have made to complete these sentences.

Water began to ________ through a hole in the roof.

The flowers began to ________ because they needed water.

When you ________, you put on your clothes.

The taxi ________ called to take Dad to the station.

Sometimes we ________ when we are asleep.

Word Puzzle

very light rain	d r _ _ _ _ _
swallow a liquid	d r _ _ _
sliding box in a piece of furniture	d r _ _ _ _
sleepy	d r _ _ _ _
die under water	d r _ _ _
pull something along	d r _ _
very bad, terrible	d r _ _ _ _ _ _

Read, Write, Learn, Cover and Spell

drain drain
droop ________
drag ________
drizzle ________
drip ________
dragon ________
driver ________
drake ________
drum ________
dream ________
drink ________
drowsy ________
drill ________
dress ________
drown ________
drop ________
drawer
____
dreadful
____

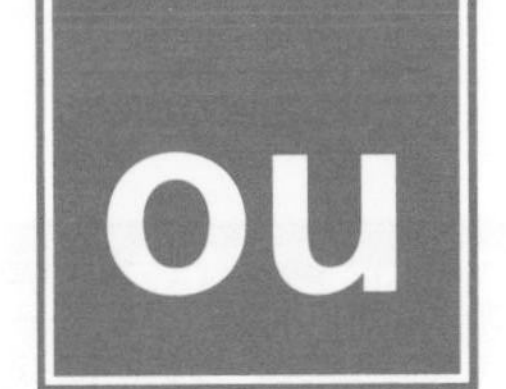

ou as in house

Read, Write, Learn, Cover and Spell

house house
south
shout
lout
mouse
cloud
trout
about
sound
spout
count
doubt
pouch
pounce
mountain
ground

Write and say **ou** ou **ou** _____ **ou** _____ **ou** _____

Add **ou** to make sixteen words.

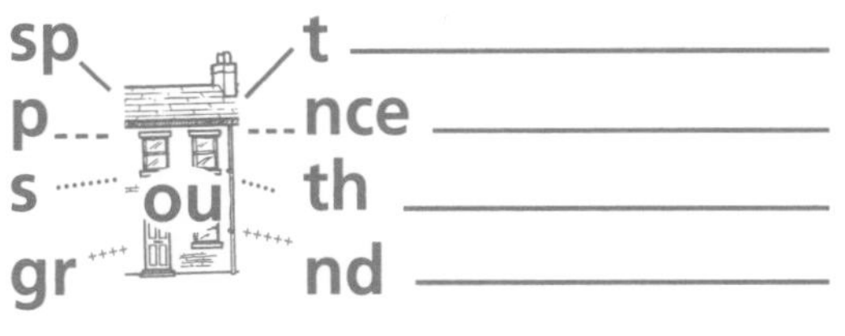

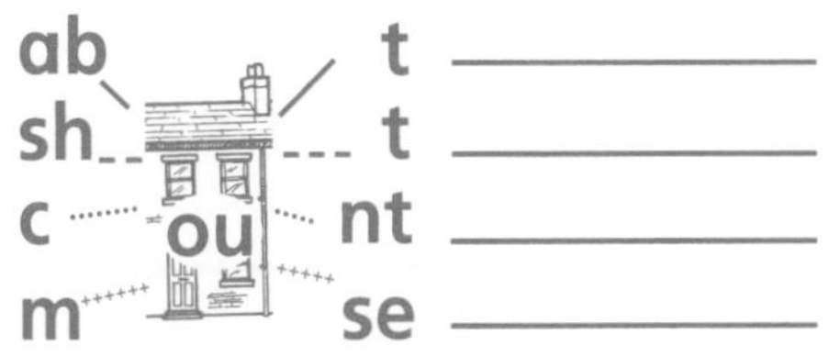

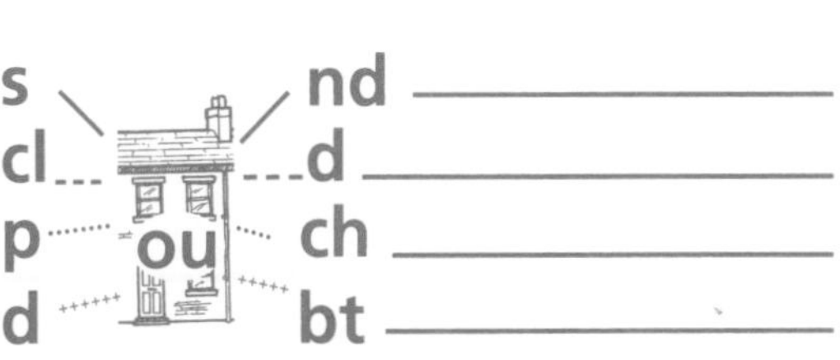

Write the correct word under each picture.

Use words you have made to complete these sentences.

Wasim arrived home__________ half past four.

Always __________your change before you leave the shop.

I saw a cat__________on a __________.

We__________that he told us the true story.

A kangaroo carries her young in a__________.

Everest is the highest __________in the world.

Crossword

							1			
						2	o	u		
							u			
				3	o	u				
		4		o	u					
				u						
5		o	u							

Clues Down

1. to add numbers
3. part of a teapot or kettle

Clues Across

2. a very small animal
3. opposite of north
4. the earth we walk on
5. fish found in rivers and lakes

au as in sausage

Write and say **au** au **au** ______ **au** ______ **au** ______

Add **au** to make fourteen words.

au — thor ______
au — tumn ______
au — dience ______

s — au — ce ______
bec — au — se ______
f — au — lt ______
astron — au — t ______

au — gust A______
au — stria A______
au — stralia A______

s — au — sage ______
l — au — nch ______
s — au — cer ______
n — au — ghty ______

Write the correct word under each picture.

______ ______ ______ ______ ______

Use words you have made to complete these sentences.

It's not my ______ we missed the bus.

______ is the largest island in the world.

I was scared ______ it was very dark.

A ______ is minced meat put inside a skin.

An ______ travels in a spaceship.

Crossword

Clues Down

2. a country in Europe
3. cup and ______.
4. something that is wrong; a mistake

Clues Across

1. not well behaved
5. eighth month of the year
6. writes books or stories
7. season before winter

Read, Write, Learn, Cover and Spell

fault	fault
author	
August	
sauce	
saucer	
Austria	
launch	
autumn	
because	
naughty	
audience	
astronaut	
sausage	
Australia	

ff as in daffodil

Read, Write, Learn, Cover and Spell

cliff	cliff
off	
sheriff	
giraffe	
traffic	
office	
offer	
stiff	
baffle	
suffer	
effort	
coffee	
buffalo	
daffodil	
different	
difficult	

Write and say **ff** ff ______ **ff** ______ **ff** ______ **ff** ______

Add **ff** to make sixteen words.

ff: gira, o, co, di — e, er, ee, icult

gira ______ e ______
o ______ er ______
co ______ ee ______
di ______ icult ______

ff: ba, e, su, tra — le, ort, er, ic

ba ______ le ______
e ______ ort ______
su ______ er ______
tra ______ ic ______

ff: di, o, bu, da — erent, ice, alo, odil

di ______ erent ______
o ______ ice ______
bu ______ alo ______
da ______ odil ______

ff: cli, sti, o, sheri

cli ______
sti ______
o ______
sheri ______

Write the correct word under each picture.

______ ______ ______ ______ ______

Use words you have made to complete these sentences.

Humpty Dumpty fell ______ a wall.

If something is ______ you need to try very hard to do it.

______ is very heavy on our roads and motorways.

Paper is easy to fold but cardboard is ______ .

Climbing a steep hill takes a lot of ______ .

Crossword

Clues Down

1. not the same
2. tallest living animal
3. say you are willing to do something
4. very popular hot drink

Clues Across

4. very steep slope of rock
5. large, wild, North American animal similar to cattle
6. having to put up with pain, sadness etc
7. puzzle someone completely

gg as in juggler

Write and say **gg** gg **gg** ____ **gg** ____ **gg** ____

Add **gg** to make sixteen words.

gg: ju, ler, bi, er, fo, y, wa, ing

gg: ja, ed, be, ing, da, er, lu, age

gg: di, er, gi, le, sta, er, go, les

gg: jo, ing, ba, age, stru, le, tobo, an

Write the correct word under each picture.

____ ____ ____ ____

Use words you have made to complete these sentences.

We felt safe as the dog was ________ its tail.

Toya cut her arm on a ________ piece of wood.

All traffic was stopped on the motorway because it was so ________ .

A ________ does clever tricks throwing and catching things.

Word Puzzle

a long flat sledge ○○○○ g g ○○

a small knife with a pointed blade ○○ g g ○○

to walk in an unsteady way ○○○ g g ○○

larger ○○ g g ○○

to make a great effort ○○○○ g g ○○

Read, Write, Learn, Cover and Spell

juggler juggler
jagged
digger
jogging
bigger
giggle
struggle
foggy
dagger
toboggan
baggage
wagging
goggles
luggage
begging
stagger

pp as in puppy

Write and say **pp** pp ____ **pp** ____ **pp** ____ **pp** ____

Add **pp** to make sixteen words.

	pp	
cho		**er** ____
ki		**er** ____
po		**y** ____
sli		**ers** ____

	pp	
su		**orter** ____
pu		**y** ____
pu		**et** ____
a		**etite** ____

	pp	
sho		**ing** ____
sli		**ery** ____
ha		**y** ____
tri		**ed** ____

	pp	
o		**osite** ____
su		**er** ____
na		**y** ____
pe		**er** ____

Write the correct word under each picture.

____ ____ ____ ____ ____

Use words you have made to complete these sentences.

I went ____ with my mum to the supermarket.

Grandad ____ on the edge of the rug and almost fell.

A ____ is another name for a helicopter.

Billy has a good ____, and can eat at any time.

We ate our ____ before going to bed.

Word Puzzle

feeling very pleased; glad — _ _ p p _

a smoked, salted fish — _ _ p p _ _

hard to hold on to or walk on — _ _ _ p p _ _ _

hot-tasting spice — _ _ p p _ _

a flower, with large, red petals — _ _ p p _

black is the ____ of white — _ p p _ _ _ _ _

Read, Write, Learn, Cover and Spell

pepper	pepper
slippery	____
puppy	____
tripped	____
slippers	____
happy	____
puppet	____
kipper	____
nappy	____
poppy	____
supper	____
shopping	____
chopper	____
supporter	____
appetite	____
opposite	____

ss as in cross

Write and say **ss** ss **ss** ____ **ss** ____ **ss** ____

Add **ss** to make sixteen words.

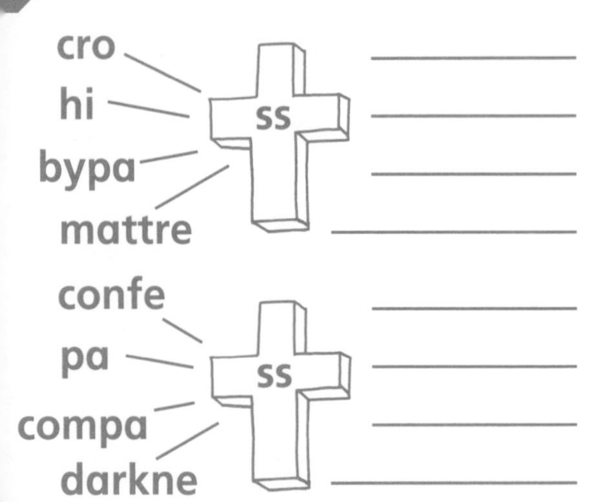

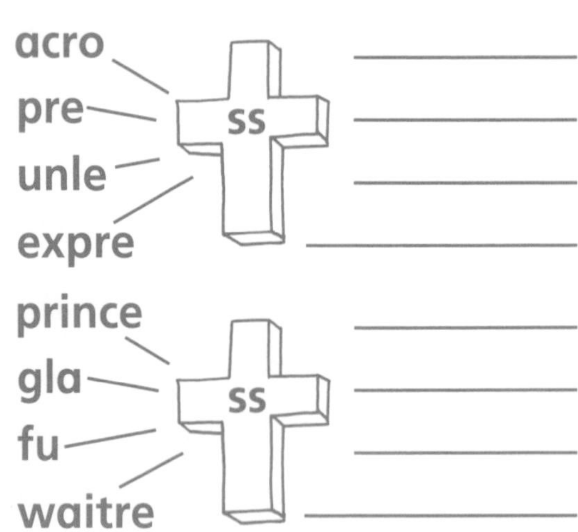

Write the correct word under each picture.

 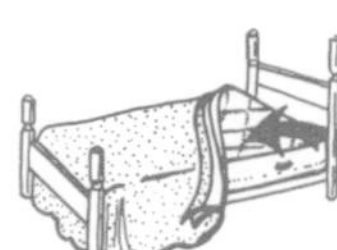 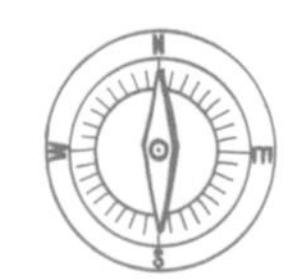  

Use words you have made to complete these sentences.

Geese and snakes ________ when they are angry.

A new bridge has been built ________ the river.

I am not going to the cinema ________ you come with me.

My dog always makes a big ________ when I come home from school.

My brother thinks he will ________ his driving test today.

Word Puzzle

thick, soft part of a bed

say that you have done wrong

to push or squeeze

used in windows

a fast train or bus

no light

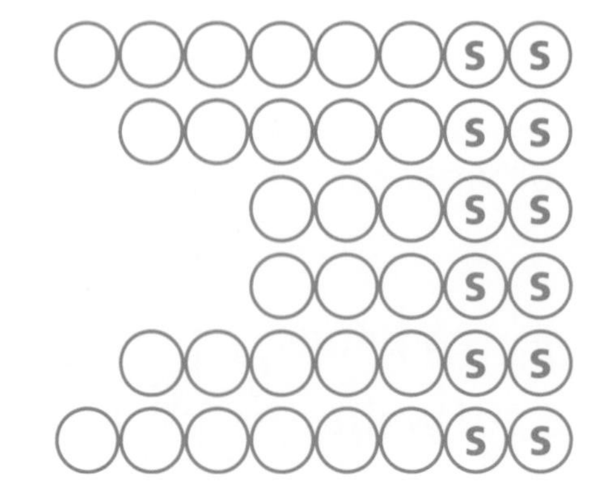

Read, Write, Learn, Cover and Spell

press press
pass
hiss
unless
glass
across
bypass
fuss
express
cross
mattress
confess
waitress
compass
darkness
princess

sc as in scarf

Write and say **sc** ___sc___ **sc** ______ **sc** ______ **sc** ______

Add **sc** to make sixteen words.

are ______
arce ______
arf ______
arecrow ______

ald ______
ab ______
ales ______
an ______

affold ______
one ______
amper ______
ulpture ______

atter ______
owl ______
ooter ______
ampi ______

Write the correct word under each picture.

______ ______ ______ ______ ______

Use words you have made to complete these sentences.

Water is ______ in hot deserts.

Many fish and reptiles are covered in ______.

Rashid had a ______ when the front door flew open.

Jason always remembers to ______ seed for the birds in winter.

When the cat appears, the mice ______ away.

Word Puzzle

a thin crust over a sore — s c _ _
burn caused by hot liquid or steam — s c _ _ _
examine carefully — s c _ _
kind of motorcycle — s c _ _ _ _ _
a small bun — s c _ _ _
an angry look on your face — s c _ _ _
large prawns — s c _ _ _ _

Read, Write, Learn, Cover and Spell

scan scan
scooter ______
scarf ______
scales ______
scampi ______
scare ______
scowl ______
scatter ______
scald ______
scab ______
scarce ______
scone ______
sculpture ______
scaffold ______
scarecrow ______
scamper ______

qu as in quilt

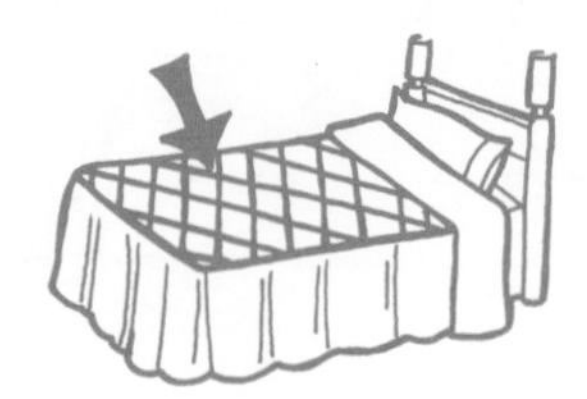

Write and say **qu** qu____ **qu** ______ **qu** ______ **qu** ______

Add **qu** to make sixteen words.

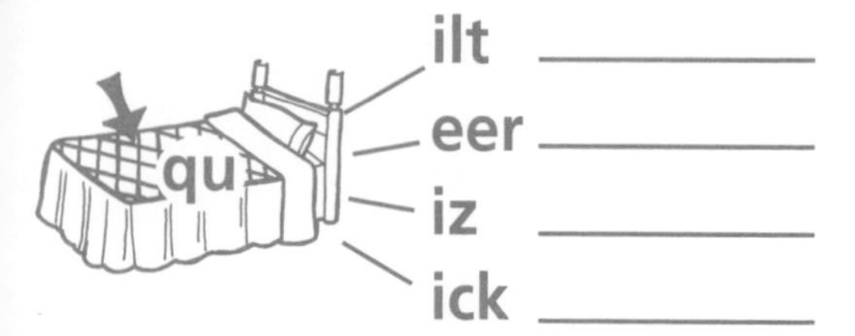

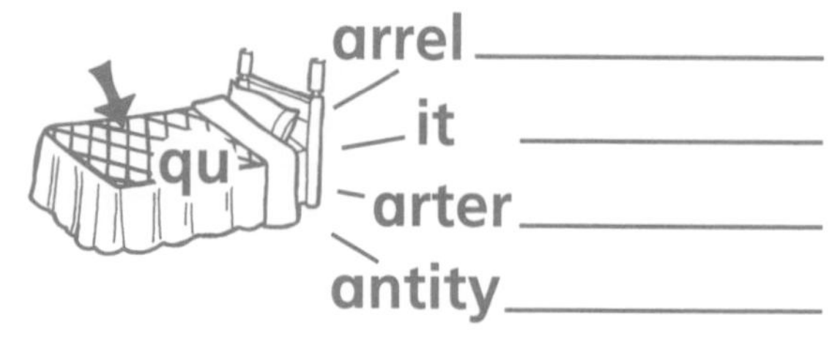

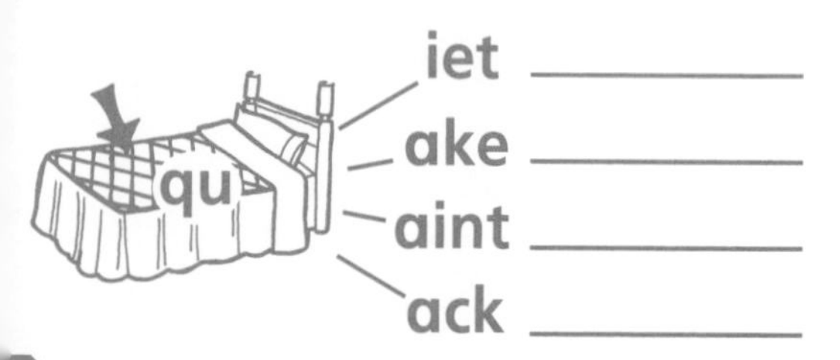

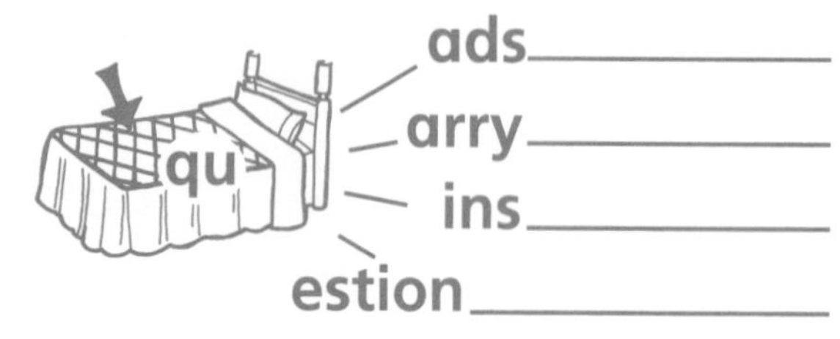

Write the correct word under each picture.

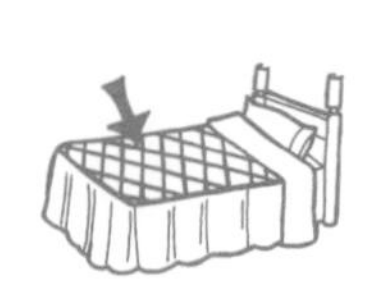

______ ______ ______ ______

Use words you have made to complete these sentences.

Fifteen minutes is a ______ of an hour.

The cat made a ______ jump towards the mouse.

The teacher answered Tessa's ______ about the story.

A ______ is a place where stone, sand etc. are dug out.

When you take part in a ______ you have to answer questions.

Word Puzzle

sound a duck makes	q u ○ ○ ○
to stop	q u ○ ○
soft, warm bed cover	q u ○ ○ ○
argue angrily with someone	q u ○ ○ ○ ○ ○
shake; tremble	q u ○ ○ ○
strange or odd in a nice way	q u ○ ○ ○ ○
without any noise	q u ○ ○ ○

sw as in swan

Write and say **sw** ~~sw~~ ____ **sw** ____ **sw** ____ **sw** ____

Add **sw** to make sixteen words.

sw: **ollen** ____, **eet** ____, **ipe** ____, **an** ____

sw: **eater** ____, **itch** ____, **eep** ____, **allow** ____

sw: **indle** ____, **ift** ____, **ap** ____, **arm** ____

sw: **ing** ____, **ear** ____, **ay** ____, **im** ____

Write the correct word under each picture.

____ ____ ____ ____ ____

Use words you have made to complete these sentences.

Wilma's face was ____ because she had the mumps.
The trees started to ____ in the strong wind.
A ____ has a forked tail and pointed wings.
Monkeys like to ____ from tree to tree.
A ____ is a knitted garment. It keeps you warm.

Word Puzzle

Clue	Answer
cheat someone	s w ○ ○ ○ ○ ○
quick	s w ○ ○ ○
change one thing for another	s w ○ ○
clean a floor etc. with a brush	s w ○ ○ ○
use rude, bad words	s w ○ ○ ○
large numberof bees together	s w ○ ○ ○
move from side to side	s w ○ ○
to hit hard	s w ○ ○ ○

Read, Write, Learn, Cover and Spell

sway sway
swift ____
sweep ____
switch ____
swim ____
swipe ____
swap ____
swan ____
swear ____
swing ____
swarm ____
sweet ____
swindle ____
sweater ____
swollen ____
swallow ____

tw as in twelve

Write and say **tw** tw ____ **tw** ____ **tw** ____ **tw** ____

Add **tw** to make sixteen words.

tw: **eezers** ____ **ig** ____ **ice** ____ **elve** ____

tw: **ilight** ____ **eet** ____ **irl** ____ **itch** ____

tw: **enty** ____ **ins** ____ **ist** ____ **ine** ____

tw: **inkle** ____ **eed** ____ **inge** ____ **itter** ____

Write the correct word under each picture.

20

____ ____ ____ ____

Use words you have made to complete these sentences.

We could hear the ________ of the birds in the trees.

Melvyn said, "Don't ________ my arm, you're hurting me."

A tiny branch of a tree is called a ________.

Jan goes to the swimming club ________ each week.

A half of twenty-four is ________.

Crossword

Clues Down

1. sound of a young bird
3. time when day is about to become night
4. thin, strong string

Clues Across

2. move with a sudden jerk
3. tool for getting hold of very small things
4. to sparkle
5. small, thin branch of a tree or shrub
6. turn round and round quickly

Read, Write, Learn, Cover and Spell

twist twist

tweed ____

twelve ____

twins ____

twig ____

twitch ____

tweet ____

twenty ____

twirl ____

twice ____

twine ____

twitter ____

twinge ____

twinkle ____

twilight ____

tweezers ____

Read, Write, Learn, Cover and Spell

walk	walk
could	
salmon	
calf	
talk	
yolk	
half	
palm	
stalk	
should	
walkers	
almond	

Add l to make twelve words.

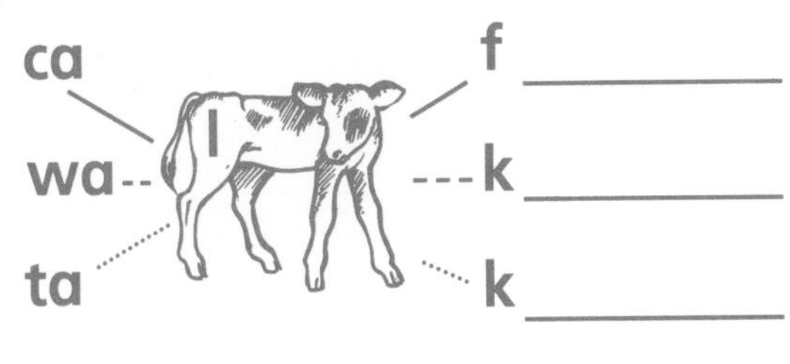

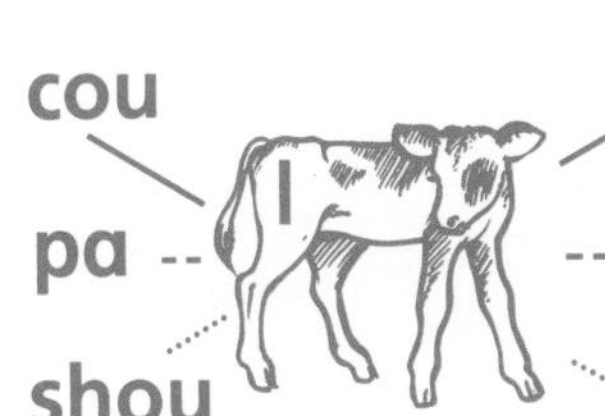
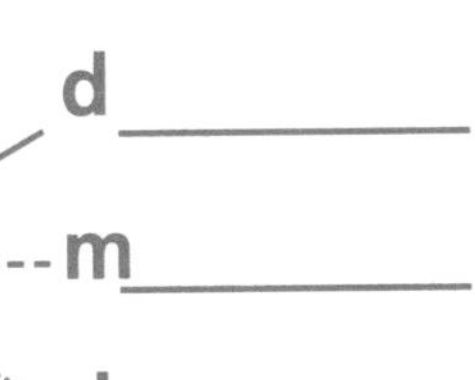

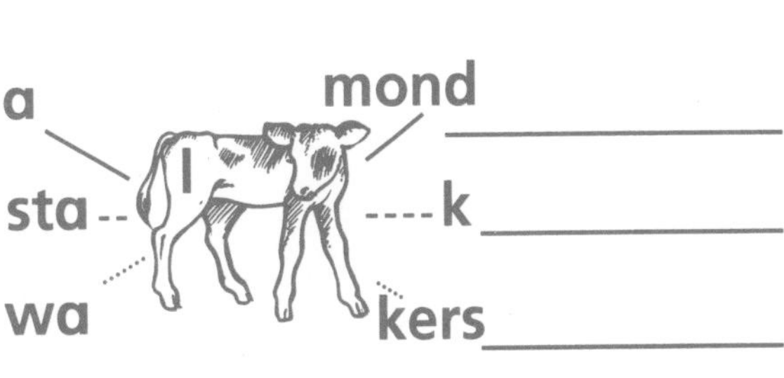

Write the correct word under each picture.

Use words you have made to complete these sentences.

Wilma ____________ be a very good swimmer if she tried harder.

We get coconuts from one kind of __________ tree.

The ____________ covered ten kilometres along the valley.

Leon likes the __________ of an egg cooked hard.

We ___________ always clean our teeth after meals.

Crosswords

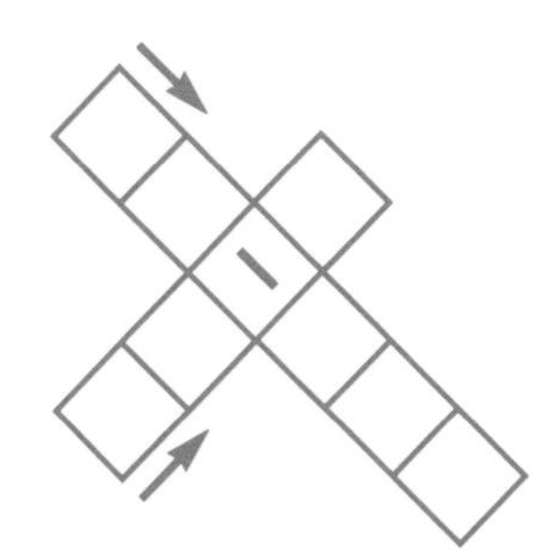

1 ↘ large fish with pink flesh

2 ↗ opposite of run

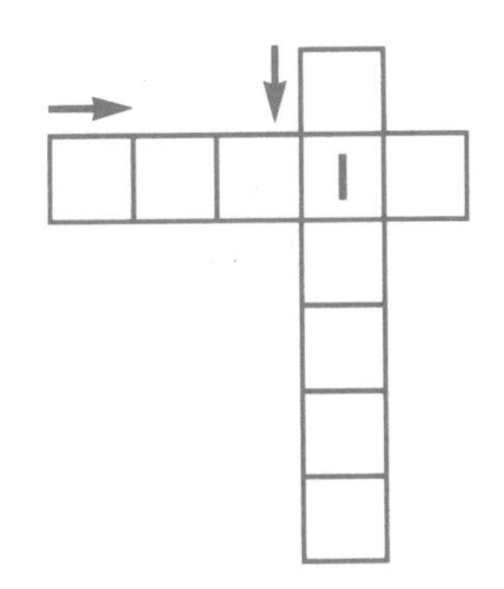

1 → main stem of a plant

2 ↓ a kind of nut

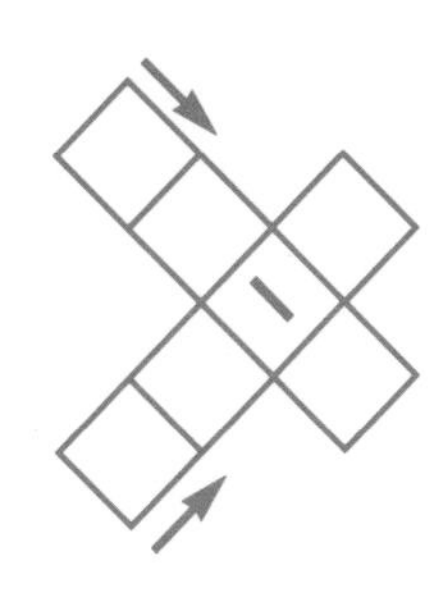

1 ↘ to speak, say things

2 ↗ tree that grows in hot countries

Silent w

Add **w** to make sixteen words.

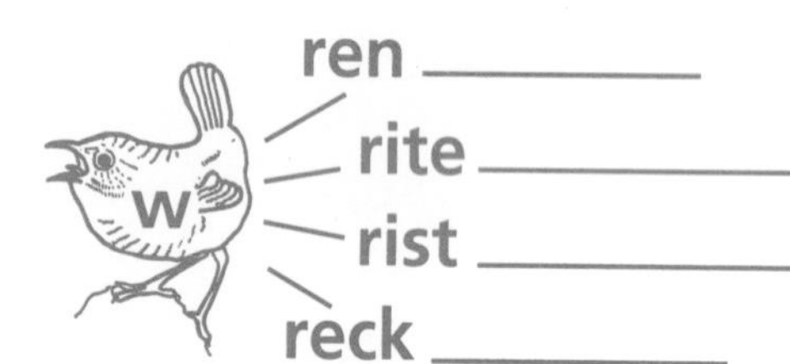

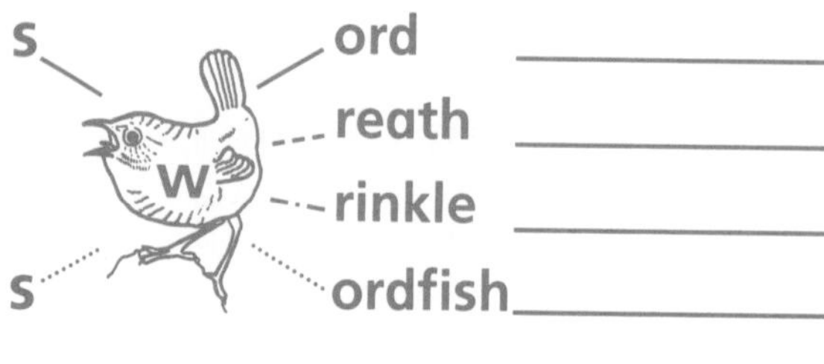

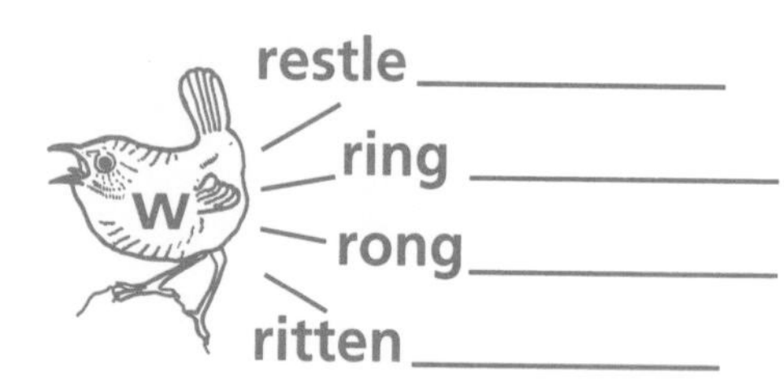

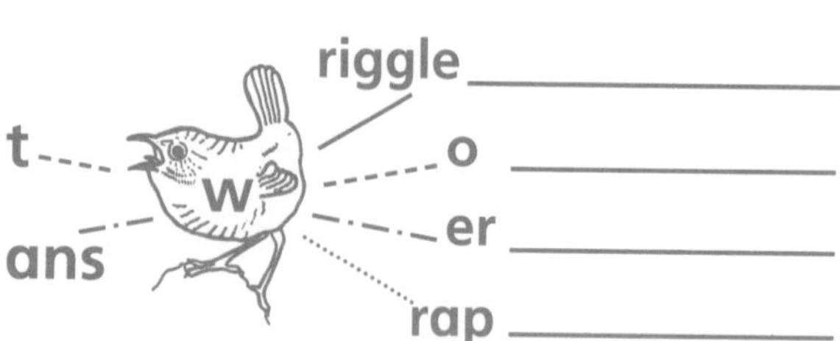

Write the correct word under each picture.

Use words you have made to complete these sentences.

I have __________ a letter to my Grandma.

It is __________ to lie and steal.

Mum asked me to __________ dad's birthday present.

The __________ to five add four is nine.

Earl cannot __________ because his __________ is broken.

Word Puzzle

you have ______ hands — △ w △

weapon with a long, steel blade — △ w △ △ △

tiny brown bird — w △ △ △

small crease in the skin — w △ △ △ △ △ △

twist and squeeze — w △ △ △ △

twist and turn you body — w △ △ △ △ △ △

what you do when you are asked something — △ △ △ w △ △

Read, Write, Learn, Cover and Spell

wrist	wrist
wrestle	
two	
wrong	
wring	
wren	
wreck	
wrap	
sword	
write	
answer	
wreath	
wriggle	
written	
wrinkle	
swordfish	

Add **and** to make sixteen words.

c	le	t	oori
p	a	d	elion
exp		h	cuffs
st		d	ruff

t	em	h	some
s	al	s	wich
g	er	isl	
l	ing	Scotl	

Write the correct word under each picture.

Use words you have made to complete these sentences.

A balloon will ____________ when it is blown up.

With only one engine working, the plane made a safe ____________.

An ____________ is land surrounded by water.

Ben Nevis is the highest mountain in ____________.

There were no chairs left at the concert so we had to ____________.

Word Puzzle

very good looking

kind of Indian cookery

a male goose

a yellow, wild flower

a two-seater bicycle

flakes of dead skin in the hair

slices of bread with a filling between them

	a	n	d					
	a	n	d					
	a	n	d					
	a	n	d					
	a	n	d					
	a	n	d					
	a	n	d					

Read, Write, Learn, Cover and Spell

gander gander

scandal

tandem

expand

stand

candle

landing

island

panda

Scotland

tandoori

dandruff

handcuffs

dandelion

handsome

sandwich

mp as in tramp

Write and say **mp** mp **mp**_____ **mp**_____ **mp**_____

Add **mp** to make sixteen words.

shri	mp	__________
swa	mp	__________
tra	mp	__________
clu	mp	__________

chi	mp	anzee	__________
Oly	mp	ics	__________
tra	mp	le	__________
cha	mp	ions	__________

tru	mp	et	__________
sca	mp	i	__________
cla	mp	ed	__________
sha	mp	oo	__________

sta	mp	ede	__________
gli	mp	se	__________
atte	mp	t	__________
pro	mp	t	__________

Write the correct word under each picture.

________ ________ ________ ________ ________

Use words you have made to complete these sentences.

The __________ are held every four years in a different country.

Manchester United have been football __________ several times.

I caught a __________ of the castle as our train went by.

A thick __________ of trees hid our view of the village.

Be careful where you park your car in case it is __________.

Word Puzzle

Clue	Letters
used for washing hair	△△△ m p △△
on time; done at once	△△△ m p △
very soft, wet ground	△△△ m p
sudden rush of frightened animals	△△△ m p △△△
to try	△△△△△ m p △
seafood like large shrimps	△△△ m p △
walk heavily on something	△△△ m p △△

Read, Write, Learn, Cover and Spell

prompt	prompt
tramp	______
glimpse	______
scampi	______
trumpet	______
attempt	______
swamp	______
clump	______
shrimp	______
chimpanzee	______
clamped	______
Olympics	______
trample	______
shampoo	______
stampede	______
champions	______

ie as in shield

Write and say **ie** ie______ **ie** ______ **ie** ______ **ie** ______

Add **ie** to make sixteen words.

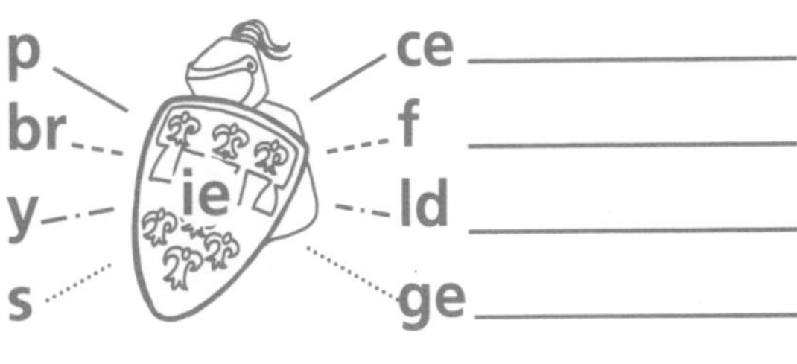

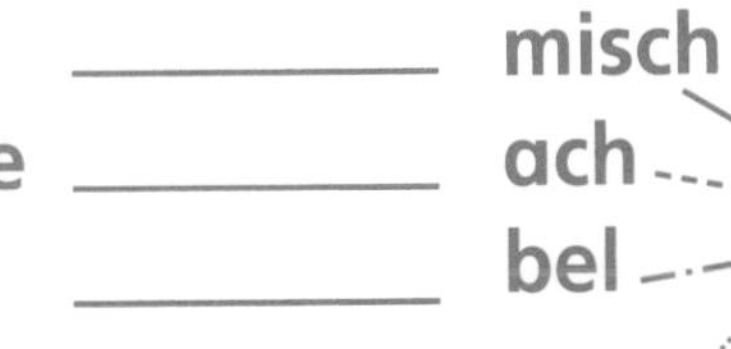

Write the correct word under each picture.

 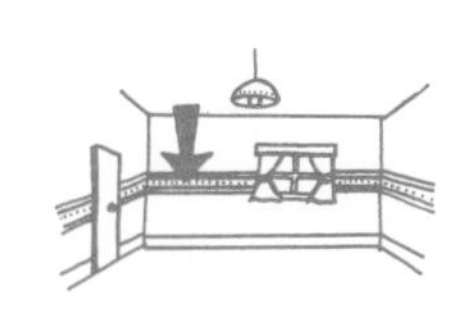  

______ ______ ______ ______

Use words you have made to complete these sentences.

A ______ is the daughter of a brother or sister.

I ______ Gordon can win the race if he has a good start.

Someone who takes things belonging to other people is a ______.

When you wipe your nose you use a ______.

I am going to ______ my aim of saving up for a mountain bike.

Word Puzzle

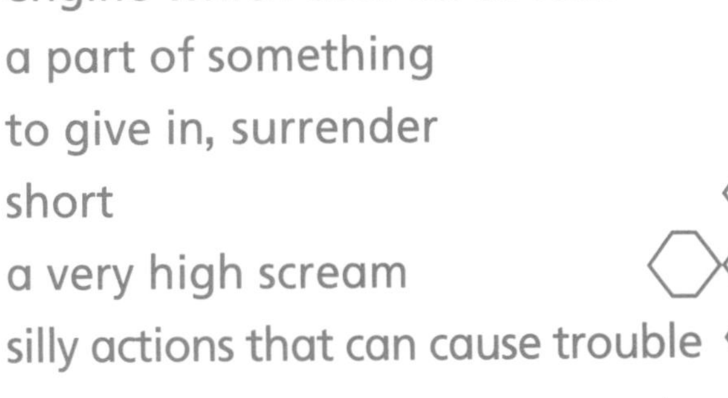

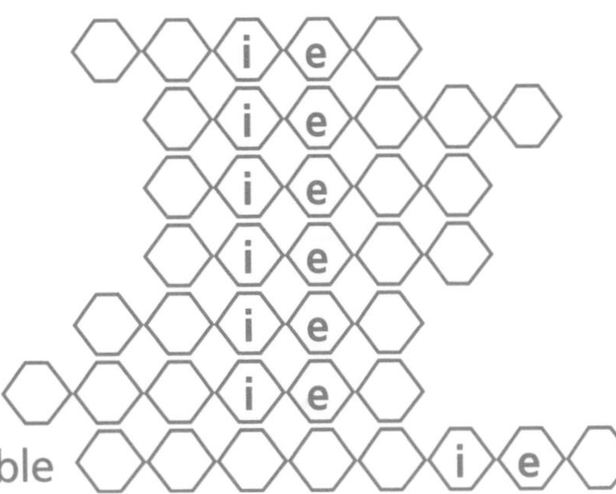

Read, Write, Learn, Cover and Spell

field	field
frieze	______
shield	______
siege	______
niece	______
thief	______
yield	______
shriek	______
diesel	______
chief	______
piece	______
brief	______
believe	______
handkerchief	______
achieve	______
mischief	______

zz as in nozzle

Read, Write, Learn, Cover and Spell

dizzy	dizzy
drizzle	
sizzle	
nozzle	
jazz	
dazzle	
buzz	
muzzle	
fizz	
puzzle	
quizzes	
blizzard	
whizzed	
buzzard	

Write and say **zz** zz **zz** ______ **zz** ______ **zz** ______

Add **zz** to make fourteen words.

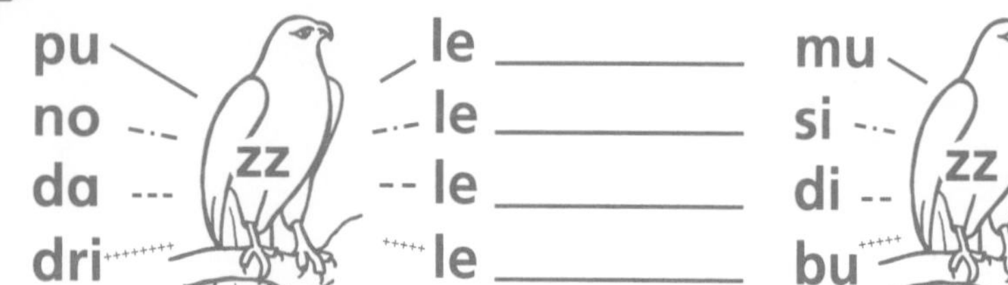

pu zz **le** ______
no zz **le** ______
da zz **le** ______
dri zz **le** ______

mu zz **le** ______
si zz **le** ______
di zz **y** ______
bu zz **ard** ______

bli zz **ard** ______
qui zz **es** ______
whi zz **ed** ______

bu zz ______
fi zz ______
ja zz ______

Write the correct word under each picture.

______ ______ ______ ______

Use words you have made to complete these sentences.

When you spin round and round quickly you may feel______.

Bees and other insects______.

My dad does a crossword______ in the paper every day.

If you look at a bright light it can______ your eyes.

An arrow______ past Robin Hood's head.

Word Puzzle

Clue								
light rain falling gently	□	□	□	z	z	□	□	
problem or question that is hard to solve		□	□	z	z	□	□	
to give off lots of little bubbles		□	□	z	z			
a type of music		□	□	z	z			
a hissing sound, as bacon in a frying pan		□	□	z	z	□	□	
a large bird of prey		□	□	z	z	□	□	□

Soft c as in dice

Add **c** to make sixteen words.

di e ____
spa e ____
pea e ____

o ean ____
bi ycle ____
De ember ____

pala e ____
pie e ____
noti e ____
advi e ____
entran e ____

ider ____
ertain ____
ease ____
ygnet ____
ymbals ____

Write the correct word under each picture.

____ ____ ____ ____ ____

Use words you have made to complete these sentences.

The Pacific ____ is the largest in the world.

If Curtley's leg is better, he is ____ to play on Saturday.

I took the teacher's ____ and joined the computer club.

The ____ says, "Keep off the grass".

In 1961, the Russian, Yuri Gagarin, was the first man to fly in ____.

Word Puzzle

Clue	Answer
to stop	c _ _ _ _
a way in	_ _ _ _ _ _ c _
part of something	_ _ _ c _
the twelfth month	_ _ c _ _ _ _ _
a young swan	c _ _ _ _ _
strong drink made from apples	c _ _ _ _

Read, Write, Learn, Cover and Spell

bicycle bicycle
space ____
advice ____
piece ____
ocean ____
cider ____
notice ____
peace ____
dice ____
certain ____
palace ____
cease ____
cygnet ____
cymbals ____
entrance ____
December ____

as in gem

Add **g** to make eighteen words.

wa … **e** ____________
spon … **e** ____________
oran … **e** ____________
sur … **eon** ____________
stran … **er** ____________

loun … **e** ____________
a … **e** ____________
chan … **e** ____________
bar … **e** ____________
frin … **e** ____________

langua … **e** ____________
hu … **e** ____________
voya … **e** ____________
oxy … **en** ____________

g … **erbil** ____________
g … **em** ____________
g … **entle** ____________
g … **iraffe** ____________

Write the correct word under each picture.

____________ ____________ ____________ ____________ ____________

Use words you have made to complete these sentences.

In France, the people speak the French ____________ .
Lisa is always ____________ with her baby sister.
A ____________ will soak up water and is used for washing.
Tadpoles ____________ into frogs.
Mum and Dad have bought a new settee and two chairs for the ____________ .

Crossword

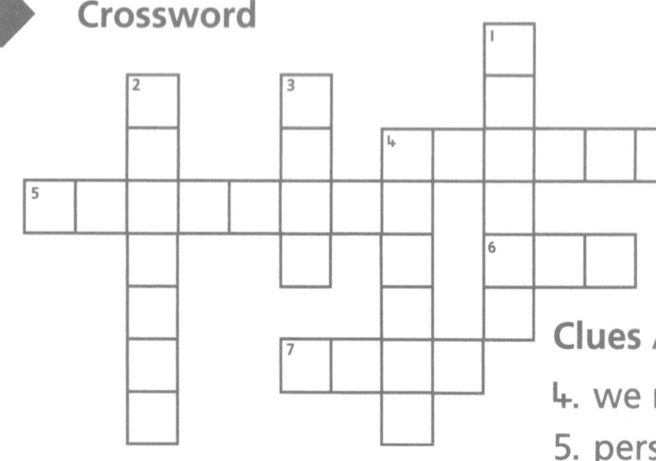

Clues Down

1. journey by sea
2. an animal with a very long neck
3. money for work done
4. sweet, juicy fruit

Clues Across

4. we need this gas to live!
5. person not known to you
6. a precious stone
7. opposite of tiny

Read, Write, Learn, Cover and Spell

wage wage
lounge ____________
age ____________
gem ____________
barge ____________
huge ____________
gerbil ____________
oxygen ____________
giraffe ____________
orange ____________
gentle ____________
change ____________
surgeon ____________
voyage ____________
sponge ____________
fringe ____________
stranger ____________
language ____________

scr as in screw

Write and say **scr** scr____ **scr**_____ **scr**_____ **scr**_____

Add **scr** to make eighteen words.

scr — ew________ ub________ ibble________

scr — amble________ oll________ ounge________

scr — uffy________ ipt________ atch________

scr — ap________ een________ eech________

scr — abble________ ooge________ ewdriver________

scr — ape________ um________ eam________

Write the correct word under each picture.

write the correct word under each picture

________ ________ ________ ________

Use words you have made to complete these sentences.

We heard the ________ of the car's brakes before the crash.

We had to ________ over the rocks to reach the shore.

Be careful the cat doesn't ________ you.

When the electricity went off, the TV ________ went blank.

Crossword

Clues Across

3. rub hard with a stiff brush
4. get things you want without paying
5. small piece
6. write carelessly
7. a mean person

Clues Down

1. it happens a lot in the game of rugby
2. loud, shrill cry
4. word game played on a board

Read, Write, Learn, Cover and Spell

screw screw
scribble ______
scruffy ______
scrap ______
scrape ______
scrum ______
screen ______
screech ______
script ______
scratch ______
scroll ______
scrub ______
scream ______
screwdriver ______
scrabble ______
scrooge ______
scramble ______
scrounge ______

str as in street

Write and say **str** str____ **str**____ **str**____ **str**____

Add **str** to make eighteen words.

str: **ength**____ **ip**____ **ay**____ **awberry**____

str: **eam**____ **aw**____ **etch**____ **uggle**____

str: **etcher**____ **ong**____ **ide**____ **ap**____ **aight**____

str: **ange**____ **oke**____ **eet**____ **ike**____ **ing**____

Write the correct word under each picture.

____ ____ ____ ____ ____

Use words you have made to complete these sentences.

Diane found a________ puppy shivering with cold at the back door.

You can____________a piece of elastic.

A ruler helps you to draw a ____________ line.

The milkman calls at most of the houses in our_________.

Grandma didn't have much ____________ after her illness.

Word Puzzle

caress gently with the hand	s t r ○ ○ ○
a flat strip of leather	s t r ○ ○
to undress	s t r ○ ○
to fight; to make a big effort	s t r ○ ○ ○ ○ ○
opposite of weak	s t r ○ ○ ○
dry, cut stalks of corn	s t r ○ ○
to hit something hard	s t r ○ ○ ○

Read, Write, Learn, Cover and Spell

stray	stray
street	____
strange	____
stride	____
strong	____
stroke	____
strip	____
straight	____
strike	____
stretch	____
strap	____
stream	____
straw	____
string	____
struggle	____
strength	____
strawberry	____
stretcher	____

squ as in square

- Write and say **squ** squ ____ **squ** ____ **squ** ____ **squ** ____

- Add **squ** to make twelve words.

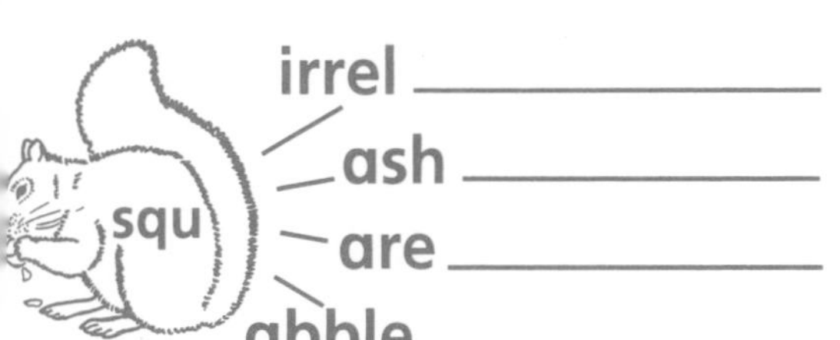

irrel ____
ash ____
are ____
abble ____

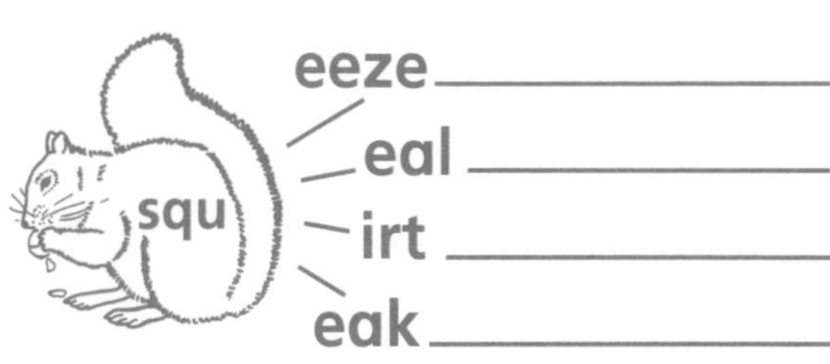

eeze ____
eal ____
irt ____
eak ____

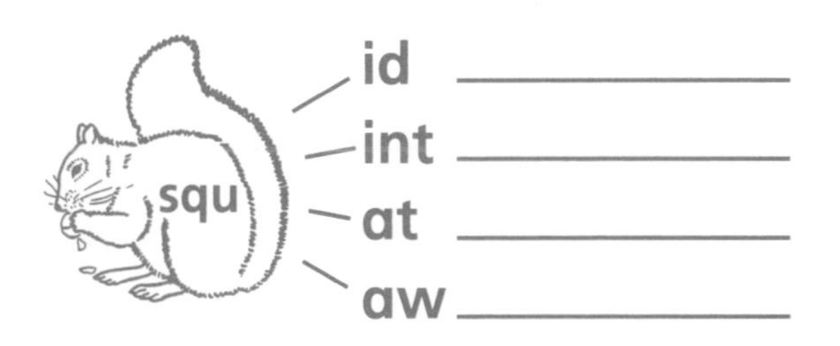

id ____
int ____
at ____
aw ____

- Write the correct word under each picture.

____ ____ ____

- Use words you have made to complete these sentences.

The strong sun shining on the snow made me ____.

I have to ____ the toothpaste tube.

Doors with hinges that need oiling often ____.

A pig will ____ when it is hurt.

A ____ is a shape with four equal sides and four right angles.

- **Word Puzzle**

Clue	Puzzle
N.American Indian woman	s q u _ _
a fruit drink	s q u _ _ _
shoot out jet of liquid	s q u _ _ _
sit on the heels	s q u _ _
a silly argument	s q u _ _ _ _ _
sea creature with ten arms	s q u _ _

Read, Write, Learn, Cover and Spell

squid	squid
squash	____
squaw	____
squeal	____
squint	____
squirt	____
squat	____
squirrel	____
squeak	____
square	____
squabble	____
squeeze	____

tch as in watch

Write and say **tch** tch **tch** ______ **tch** ______ **tch** ______

Add **tch** to make sixteen words.

wi, ma, i, pa — **tch** ______ ______ ______ ______

sna, tha, ske, sco — **tch** ______ ______ ______ ______

swi, di, wa, fe — **tch** ______ ______ ______ ______

bi, bu, ke, cru — **tch** — er, up, es ______ ______ ______ ______

Write the correct word under each picture.

______ ______ ______ ______ ______

Use words you have made to complete these sentences.

I asked my Grandma to sew a ______ on my jeans.

All my friends like tomato ______ on hamburgers and chips.

Mum asked me to ______ her coat from the wardrobe.

The light wouldn't work because the ______ was broken.

Your socks don't ______. One is red and the other is green.

Crossword

Clues Across

2. a female dog
3. a type of whisky made in Scotland
4. straw or reeds used to make a roof
5. draw quickly

Clues Down

1. makes you want to scratch it!
2. sells meat
3. grab quickly

Read, Write, Learn, Cover and Spell

match match
watch ______
patch ______
ditch ______
fetch ______
scotch ______
bitch ______
witch ______
thatch ______
snatch ______
sketch ______
itch ______
switch ______
ketchup ______
butcher ______
crutches ______

as in tent

Write and say **nt** nt ______ **nt** ______ **nt** ______ **nt** ______

Add **nt** to make eighteen words.

	nt
elepha	______
accide	______
prese	______
urge	______
ancie	______

	nt
inve	______
sile	______
spri	______
pa	______
pla	______

	nt
pare	______
patie	______
infa	______
mome	______

	nt
joi	______
te	______
poi	______
hu	______

Write the correct word under each picture.

______ ______ ______ ______ ______

Use words you have made to complete these sentences.

Young lions have to learn to ______ for their food.

A ______ is someone who is ill and is being looked after by a doctor.

My young brother, Binoy, starts at the ______ school next week.

The ankle is the ______ between the foot and the leg.

Our dog always starts to ______ in very hot weather.

Word Puzzle

Clue	Answer
a mother or father	○○○○ⓝⓣ
needs to be dealt with at once	○○○○ⓝⓣ
without any sound	○○○○ⓝⓣ
sharp end of something	○○○ⓝⓣ
very old	○○○○○○ⓝⓣ
to run very fast	○○○○ⓝⓣ
a very short time	○○○○ⓝⓣ

Read, Write, Learn, Cover and Spell

joint	joint
present	______
urgent	______
pant	______
invent	______
sprint	______
point	______
ancient	______
patient	______
silent	______
tent	______
parent	______
hunt	______
infant	______
plant	______
accident	______
elephant	______
moment	______

age as in cottage  and stage 

Add **age** to make eighteen words.

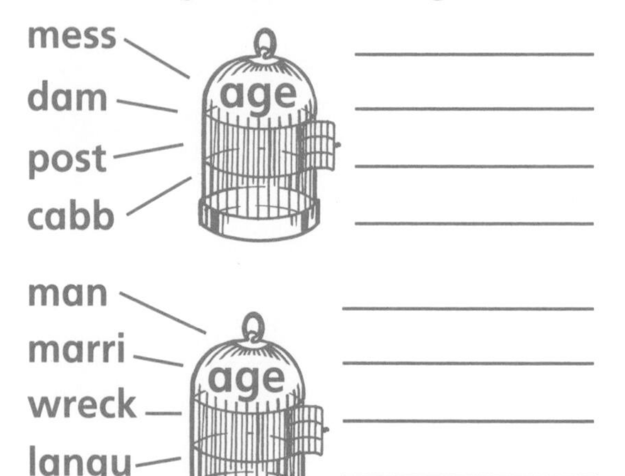

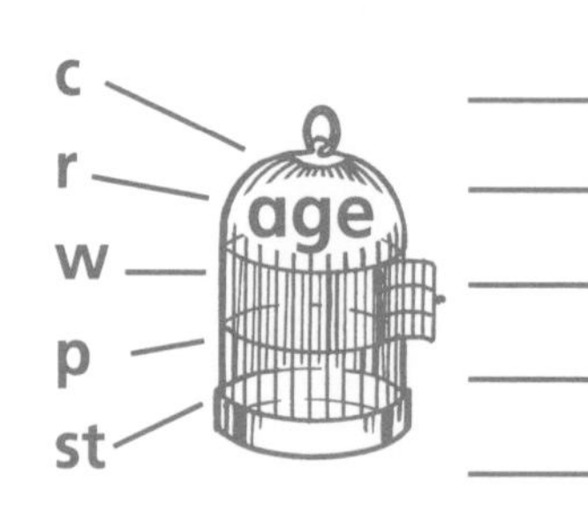

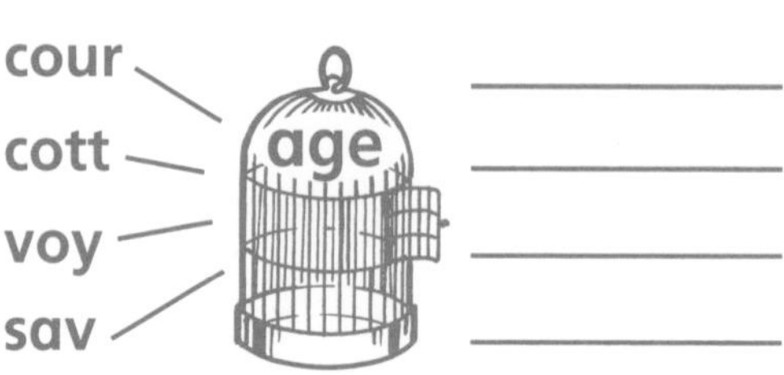

Write the correct word under each picture.

Use words you have made to complete these sentences.

The hard frost did a lot of __________ to the farmer's crops.

Mum sent a __________ to the teacher to say I was ill.

The English __________ is spoken in many parts of the world.

The beach was covered with the __________ of the ship.

The books are heavy but I'm sure Ravi will __________ to carry them.

Crossword

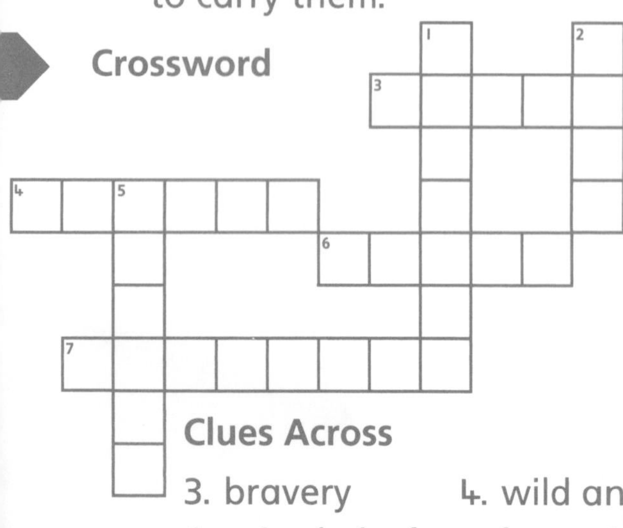

Clues Down

1. charge for sending letters or packages by mail
2. money paid for work done
5. a long journey, usually by sea

Clues Across

3. bravery
4. wild and fierce
6. raised platform for acting, dancing, etc
7. a wedding

Read, Write, Learn, Cover and Spell

page page
cage
wage
rage
stage
cabbage
damage
savage
courage
postage
cottage
sausage
message
manage
voyage
marriage
wreckage
language

al as in medal

- Write and say **al** al ______ **al** ______ **al** ______ **al** ______

- Add **al** to make sixteen words.

sign	**al**	______
equ		______
annu		______
loy		______

centr	**al**	______
fin		______
sand		______
capit		______

med	**al**	______
vand		______
arriv		______
mamm		______

sever	**al**	______
met		______
anim		______
hospit		______

- Write the correct word under each picture.

______ ______ ______ ______

- Use words you have made to complete these sentences.

London is the ______ of England.
Iron, gold, silver and copper are kinds of ______.
Justine is a ______ friend. You can always count on her.
We waited for the plane's ______ at the airport.
There are ______ kinds of roses in our garden.
The slide and swings in the park were destroyed by a ______.

- **Word Puzzle**

Clue	Answer
in the middle	_ _ _ _ _ a l
the same as	_ _ _ a l
a living creature	_ _ _ _ a l
the whale is the largest	_ _ _ _ a l
happening every year	_ _ _ _ a l
the last; the end	_ _ _ a l

Read, Write, Learn, Cover and Spell

metal	metal
annual	______
capital	______
medal	______
central	______
signal	______
loyal	______
final	______
equal	______
vandal	______
sandal	______
arrival	______
animal	______
mammal	______
several	______
hospital	______

Schofield&Sims

the long-established educational publisher
specialising in maths, English and science materials for schools

Key Spelling is a series of graded activity books containing puzzles and problems that will reinforce children's essential spelling skills and knowledge.

Key Spelling Book 3 covers:

- Vowel sounds made by more than one letter (for example, 'au' and 'ie')
- Letter blends such as 'dr', 'sc' and 'mp'
- Word endings (for example, 'tch' and 'age')
- Silent letters (for example, 'l' as in 'should')
- Soft letters (for example, 'c' as in 'dice').

This book is suitable for children in Key Stage 2.

The full range of titles in the series is as follows:

Key Spelling Book 1:	ISBN 978 07217 0841 6
Key Spelling Book 2:	ISBN 978 07217 0842 3
Key Spelling Book 3:	ISBN 978 07217 0843 0
Key Spelling Book 4:	ISBN 978 07217 0844 7

Have you tried **Springboard** by Schofield & Sims?
This is a series of graded activity books reinforcing key aspects of literacy such as sentence construction, vocabulary and reading comprehension.

For further information and to place your order visit www.schofieldandsims.co.uk or telephone 01484 607080

ISBN 978-07217-0843-0
9 780721 708430

Schofield&Sims

Dogley Mill, Fenay Bridge, Huddersfield HD8 0NQ
Phone: 01484 607080 Facsimile: 01484 606815
E-mail: sales@schofieldandsims.co.uk
www.schofieldandsims.co.uk

ISBN 978 07217 0843 0

£2.45 (Retail price)

Key Stage 2
Age range: 7–11 years